Selections from

PAUL WELLER MODERN CLASSiCS
THE GREATEST HiTS

GUITAR
TAB
EDITION

GW00642604

WISE PUBLICATIONS
LONDON/NEW YORK/SYDNEY/PARIS/COPENHAGEN/MADRID

guitar tablature explained

Guitar music can be notated three different ways: on a musical stave, in tablature, and in rhythm slashes

RHYTHM SLASHES are written above the stave. Strum chords in the rhythm indicated. Round noteheads indicate single notes.

THE MUSICAL STAVE shows pitches and rhythms and is divided by lines into bars. Pitches are named after the first seven letters of the alphabet.

TABLATURE graphically represents the guitar fingerboard. Each horizontal line represents a string, and each number represents a fret.

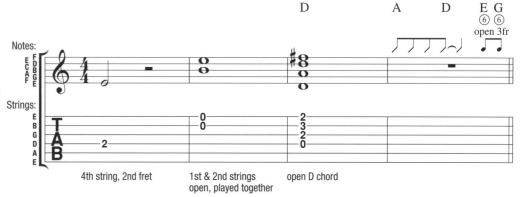

4th string, 2nd fret   1st & 2nd strings open, played together   open D chord

definitions for special guitar notation

SEMI-TONE BEND: Strike the note and bend up a semi-tone (1/2 step).

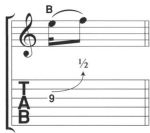

WHOLE-TONE BEND: Strike the note and bend up a whole-tone (whole step).

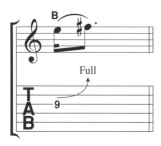

GRACE NOTE BEND: Strike the note and bend as indicated. Play the first note as quickly as possible.

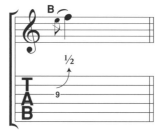

QUARTER-TONE BEND: Strike the note and bend up a 1/4 step.

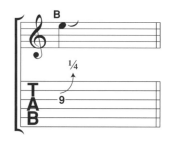

BEND & RELEASE: Strike the note and bend up as indicated, then release back to the original note.

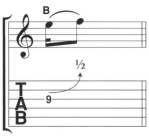

COMPOUND BEND & RELEASE: Strike the note and bend up and down in the rhythm indicated.

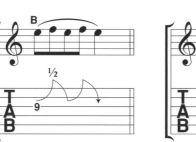

PRE-BEND: Bend the note as indicated, then strike it.

PRE-BEND & RELEASE: Bend the note as indicated. Strike it and release the note back to the original pitch.

UNISON BEND: Strike the two notes simultaneously and bend the lower note up to the pitch of the higher.

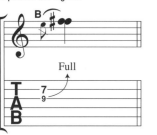

BEND & RESTRIKE: Strike the note and bend as indicated then restrike the string where the symbol occurs.

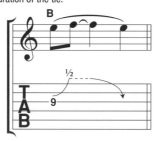

BEND, HOLD AND RELEASE: Same as bend and release but hold the bend for the duration of the tie.

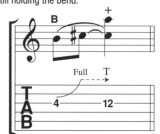

BEND AND TAP: Bend the note as indicated and tap the higher fret while still holding the bend.

VIBRATO: The string is vibrated by rapidly bending and releasing the note with the fretting hand.

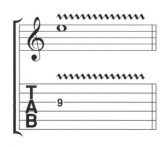

HAMMER-ON: Strike the first (lower) note with one finger, then sound the higher note (on the same string) with another finger by fretting it without picking.

PULL-OFF: Place both fingers on the notes to be sounded, Strike the first note and without picking, pull the finger off to sound the second (lower) note.

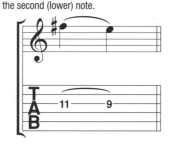

LEGATO SLIDE (GLISS): Strike the first note and then slide the same fret-hand finger up or down to the second note. The second note is not struck.

NOTE: The speed of any bend is indicated by the music notation and tempo.

SHIFT SLIDE (GLISS & RESTRIKE): Same as legato slide, except the second note is struck.

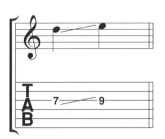

TRILL: Very rapidly alternate between the notes indicated by continuously hammering on and pulling off.

TAPPING: Hammer ("tap") the fret indicated with the pick-hand index or middle finger and pull off to the note fretted by the fret hand.

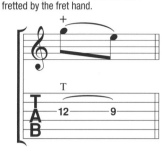

PICK SCRAPE: The edge of the pick is rubbed down (or up) the string, producing a scratchy sound.

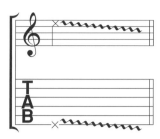

MUFFLED STRINGS: A percussive sound is produced by laying the fret hand across the string(s) without depressing, and striking them with the pick hand.

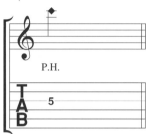

NATURAL HARMONIC: Strike the note while the fret-hand lightly touches the string directly over the fret indicated.

PINCH HARMONIC: The note is fretted normally and a harmonic is produced by adding the edge of the thumb or the tip of the index finger of the pick hand to the normal pick attack.

HARP HARMONIC: The note is fretted normally and a harmonic is produced by gently resting the pick hand's index finger directly above the indicated fret (in parentheses) while the pick hand's thumb or pick assists by plucking the appropriate string.

PALM MUTING: The note is partially muted by the pick hand lightly touching the string(s) just before the bridge.

RAKE: Drag the pick across the strings indicated with a single motion.

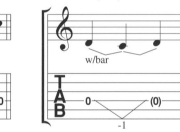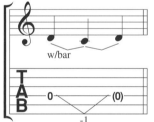

TREMOLO PICKING: The note is picked as rapidly and continuously as possible.

ARPEGGIATE: Play the notes of the chord indicated by quickly rolling them from bottom to top.

SWEEP PICKING: Rhythmic downstroke and/or upstroke motion across the strings.

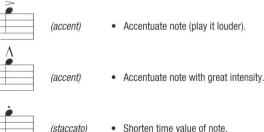

VIBRATO DIVE BAR AND RETURN: The pitch of the note or chord is dropped a specific number of steps (in rhythm) then returned to the original pitch.

VIBRATO BAR SCOOP: Depress the bar just before striking the note, then quickly release the bar.

VIBRATO BAR DIP: Strike the note and then immediately drop a specific number of steps, then release back to the original pitch.

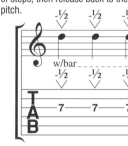

additional musical definitions

D.%. al Coda

- Go back to the sign (%), then play until the bar marked *To Coda* ⊕ then skip to the section marked ⊕ *Coda*.

D.C. al Fine

- Go back to the beginning of the song and play until the bar marked *Fine* (end).

tacet

- Instrument is silent (drops out).

- Repeat bars between signs.

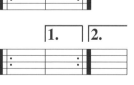

- When a repeated section has different endings, play the first ending only the first time and the second ending only the second time.

	(accent)	• Accentuate note (play it louder).
	(accent)	• Accentuate note with great intensity.
	(staccato)	• Shorten time value of note.
		• Downstroke
V		• Upstroke

NOTE: Tablature numbers in parentheses mean: 1. The note is sustained, but a new articulation (such as hammer on or slide) begins.
2. A note may be fretted but not necessarily played.

out of the sinking

WORDS & MUSIC BY PAUL WELLER

Lyrics:
'Cross the wa-ter,— there's a boat that— will take us a-way.—

Yeah, yeah,— yeah,— yeah.—

Is it shout-ing for me?—

peacock suit

WORDS & MUSIC BY PAUL WELLER

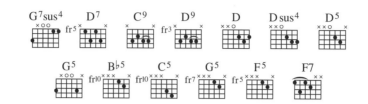

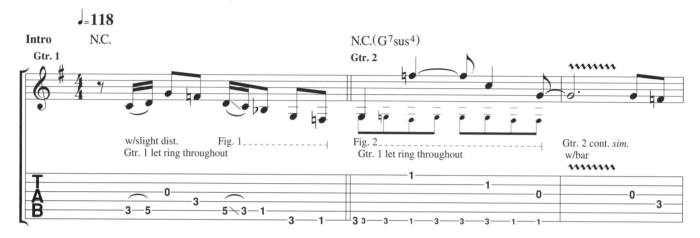

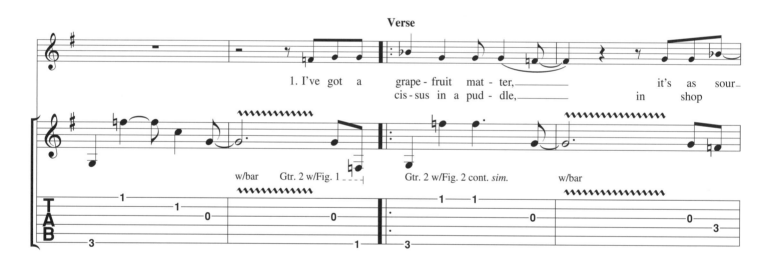

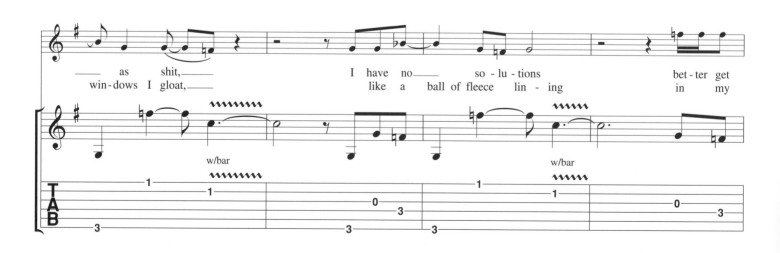

I look real cute.

w/bar

Gtr. 1 cont. in slashes

D   D sus⁴   D   D sus⁴

Gtr. 1

w/ad lib. vocal

Gtr. 2

ff let ring _ sim.

D   D sus⁴   D   D⁵

Full   Full   Full Full Full

N.C.(G⁷sus⁴)

3. Ne - me -

Gtr. 1 w/volume swells   Gtr. 1 plays Fig. 3   Gtr. 1

Gtr. 2 tacet

14

in my pea-cock suit,

did you think I should?

Outro

N.C.(F⁷)

Pea-cock suit, yeah. Pea-cock suit, yeah.

Repeat ad lib. to fade

brushed

WORDS & MUSIC BY PAUL WELLER, STEVE WHITE & MARK NELSON

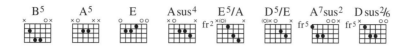

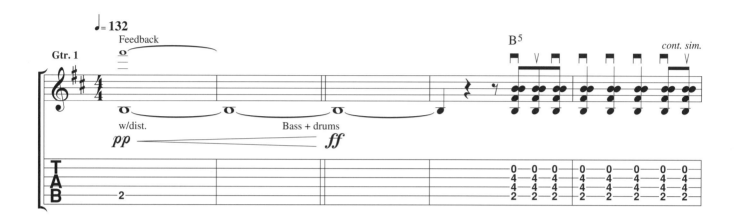

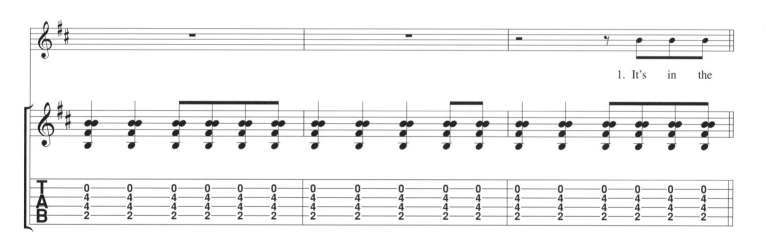

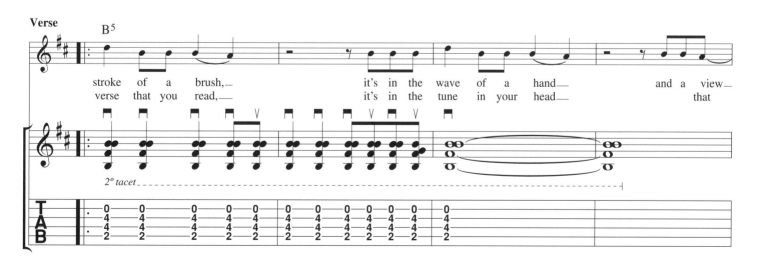

sunflower

WORDS & MUSIC BY PAUL WELLER

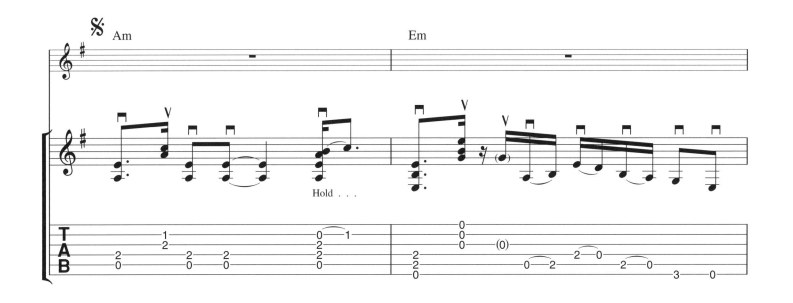

Verse:

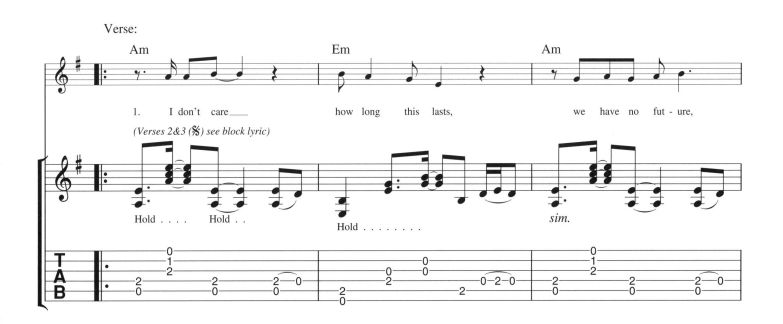

1. I don't care___ how long this lasts, we have no fut - ure,

(Verses 2&3 (𝄋) see block lyric)

Hold . . . . Hold . . Hold . . . . *sim.*

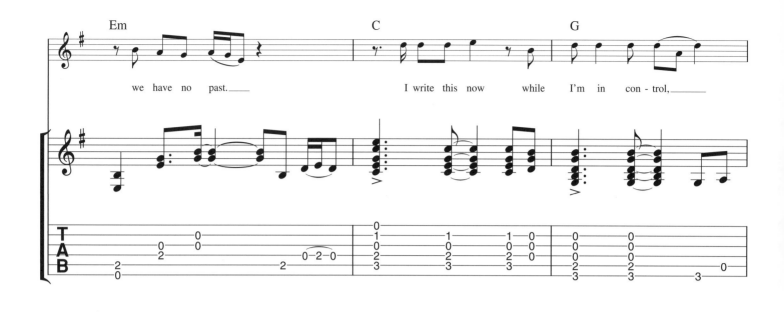

we have no past.___ I write this now while I'm in con - trol,___

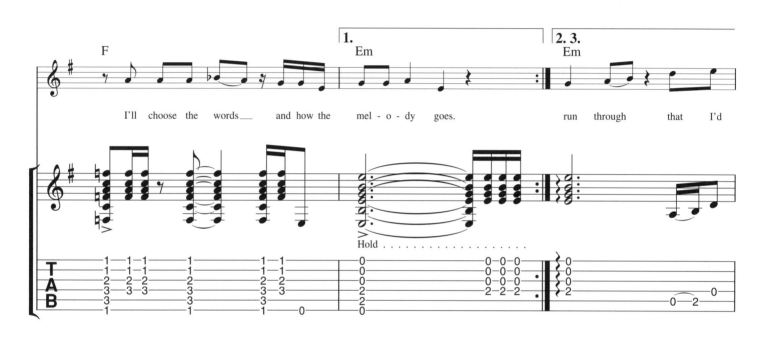

I'll choose the words___ and how the mel - o - dy goes. run through that I'd

Chorus:

run through.___ And I miss you so, and I

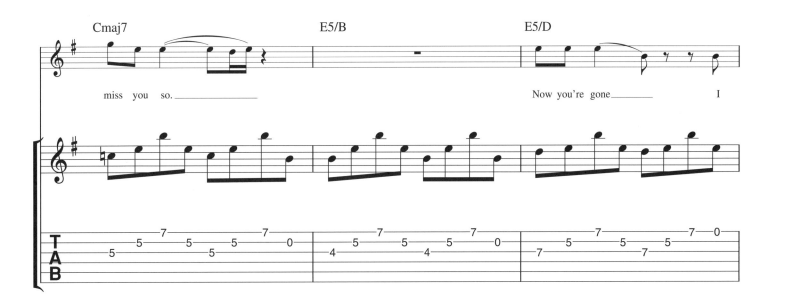

miss you so._____ Now you're gone_____ I

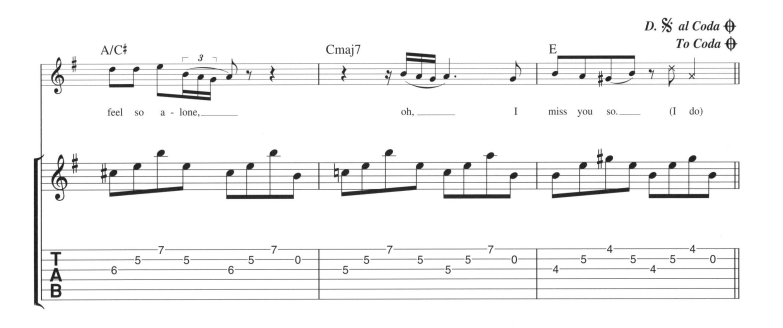

feel so a-lone,_____ oh, _____ I miss you so._____ (I do)

D. %S al Coda ⊕
To Coda ⊕

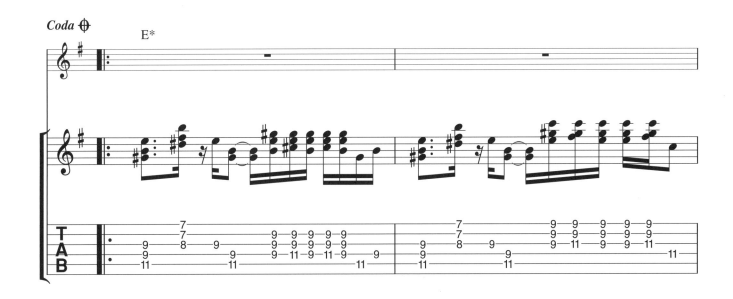

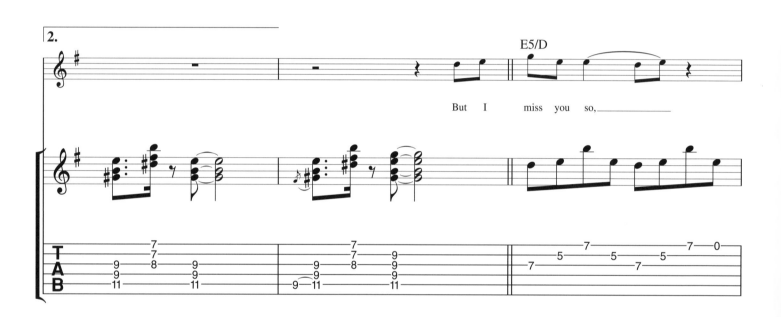

But I   miss you so,_____

oh,____ wo-man I   miss you so. ____

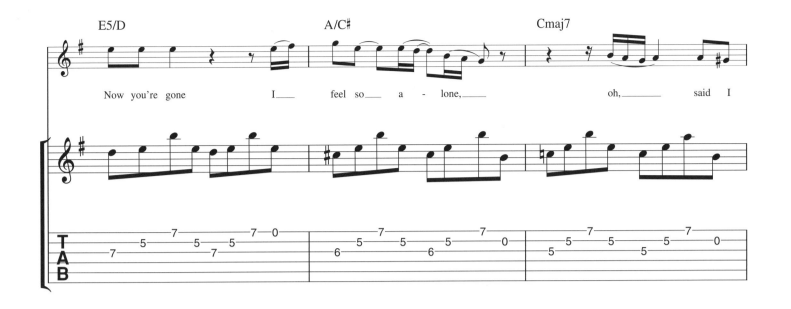

Now you're gone I__ feel so a - lone,___ oh,___ said I

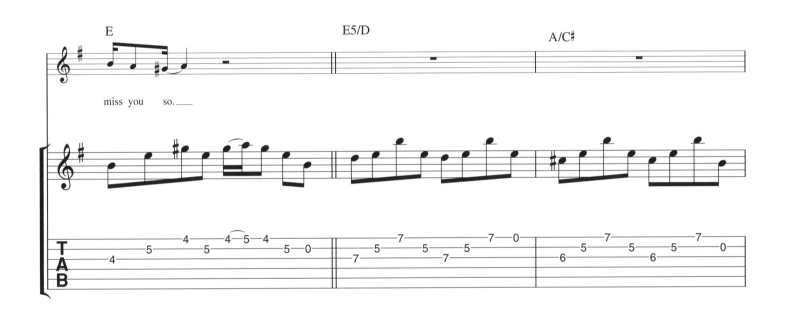

miss you so.___

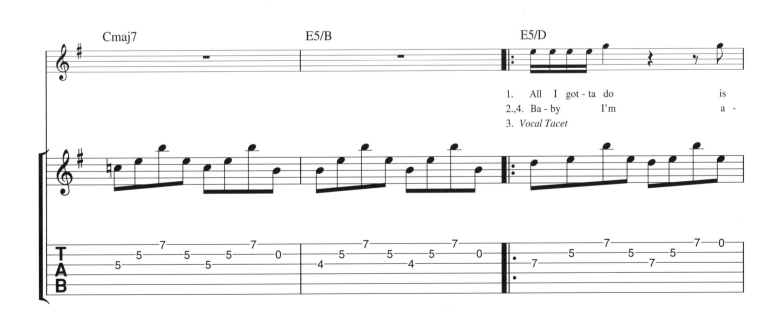

1. All I got - ta do is
2.,4. Ba - by I'm a -
3. *Vocal Tacet*

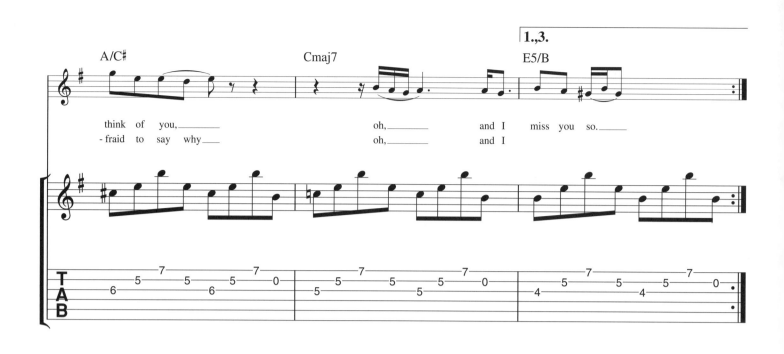

think of you,_____ oh,_____ and I miss you so._____
- fraid to say why_____ oh,_____ and I

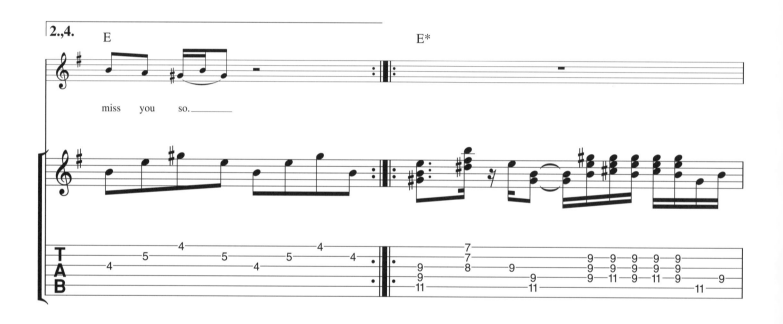

miss you so._____

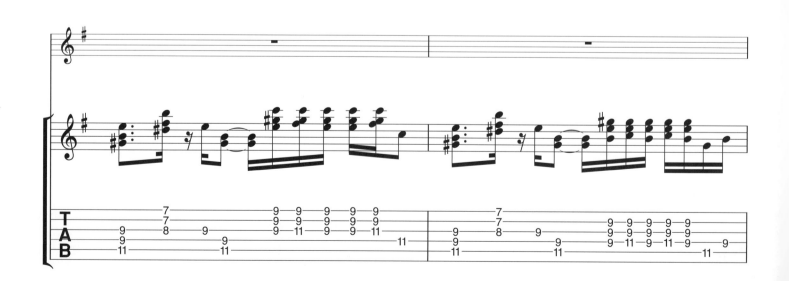

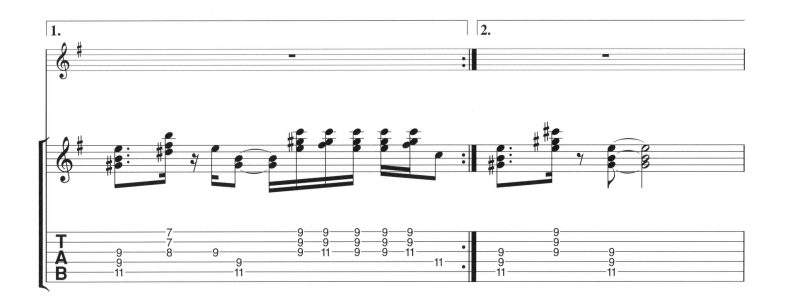

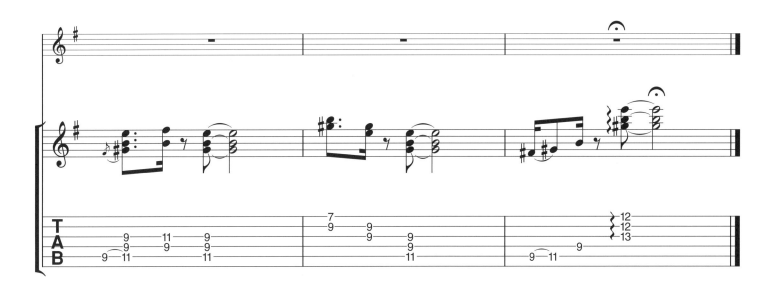

Verse 2:

Along winding streets we walked hand in hand

And how I long for that sharp wind to take my breath away again

I'd run my fingers through your hair

Hair like a wheatfield, I'd run through.

Verse 3(𝄋)

I'd send you a flower, a sunflower bright

While you cloud my days, messing up my nights

And all the way up to the top of your head

Sun-shower kisses I felt we had.

wild wood

WORDS & MUSIC BY PAUL WELLER

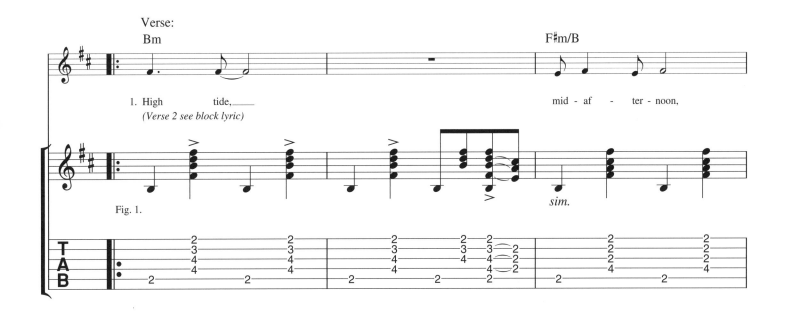

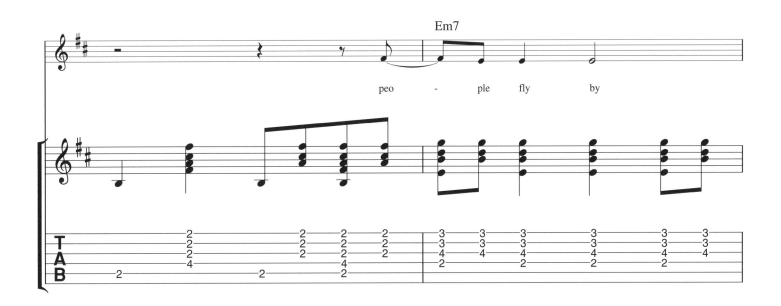

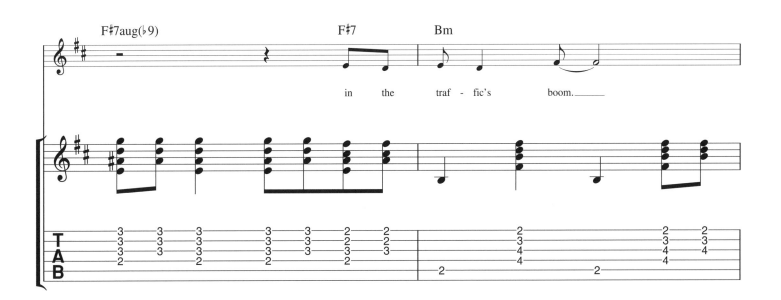

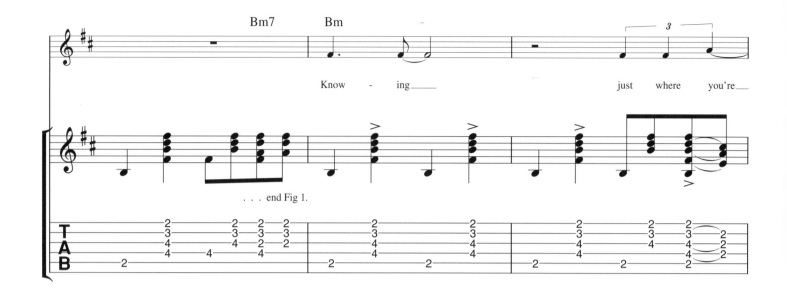

Bm7   Bm

Know - ing   just   where   you're

. . . end Fig 1.

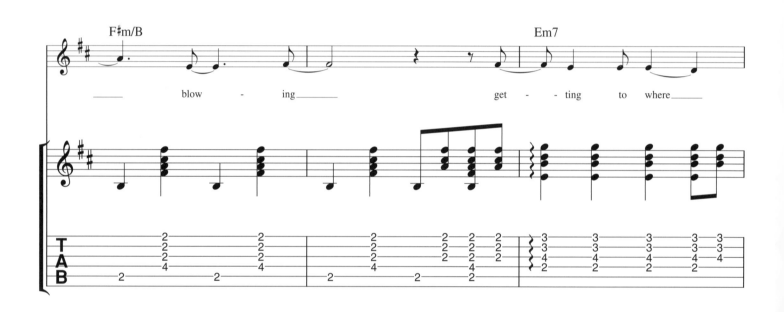

F#m/B   Em7

blow - ing   get - ting   to   where

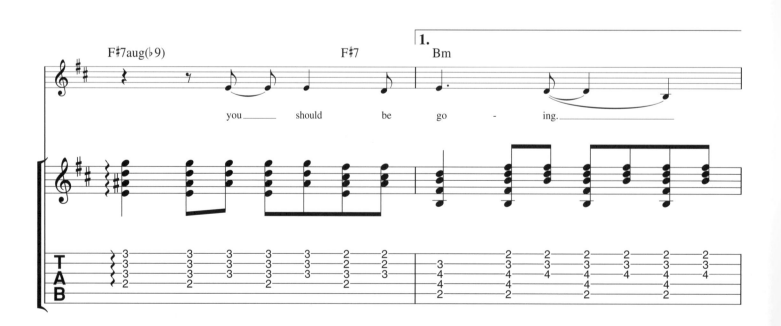

F#7aug(♭9)   F#7   **1.**
                                                Bm

you   should   be   go - ing.

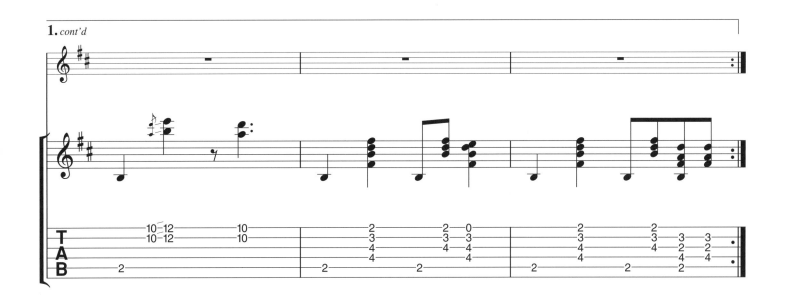

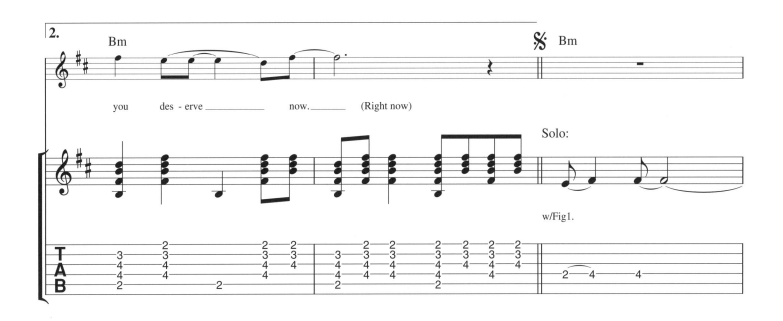

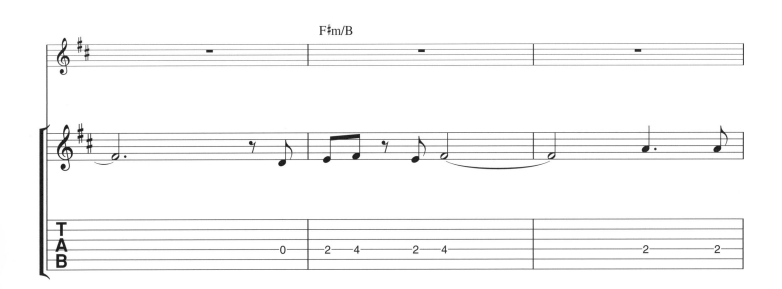

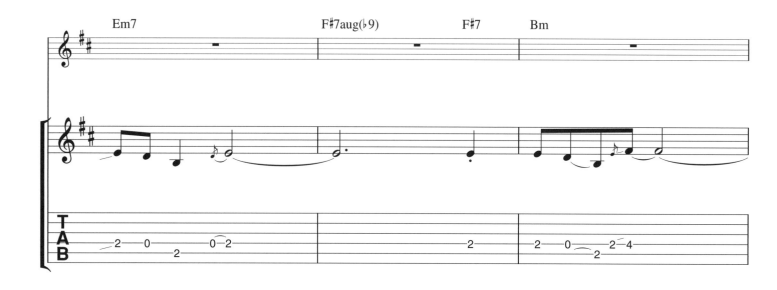

Verse:

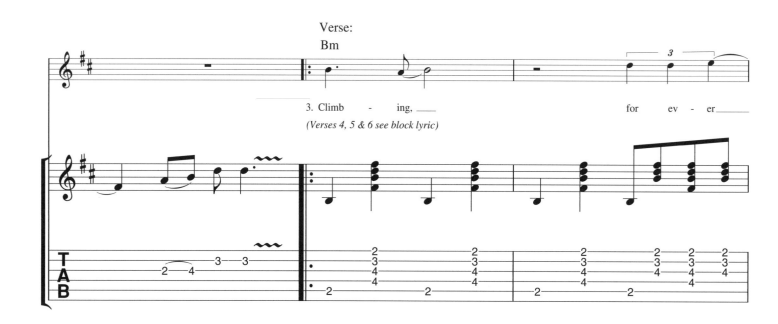

3. Climb - ing, _____ for ev - er_____

(Verses 4, 5 & 6 see block lyric)

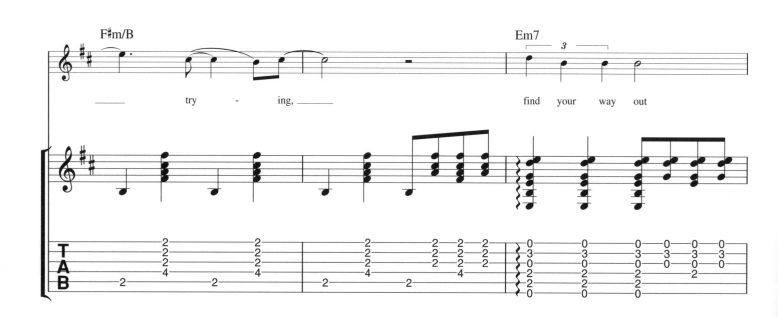

_____ try - ing, _____ find your way out

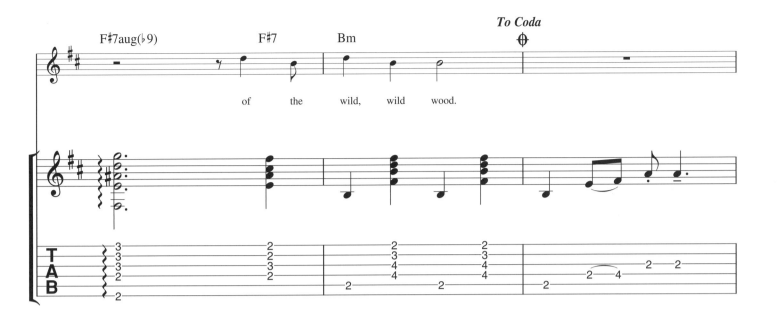

of the wild, wild wood.

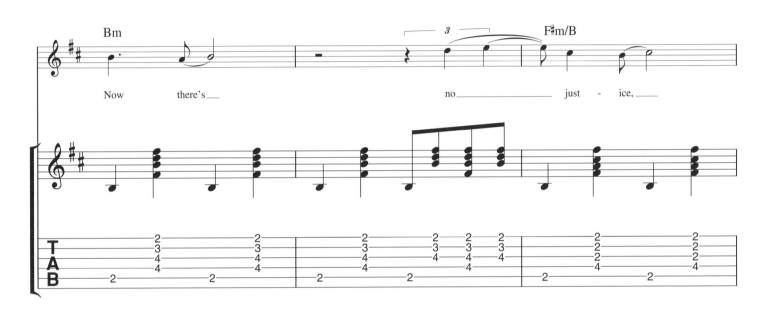

Now there's ___ no ___ just - ice, ___

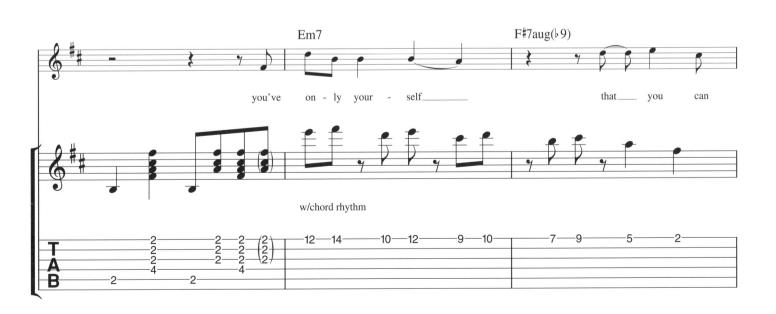

you've on - ly your - self ___ that ___ you can

w/chord rhythm

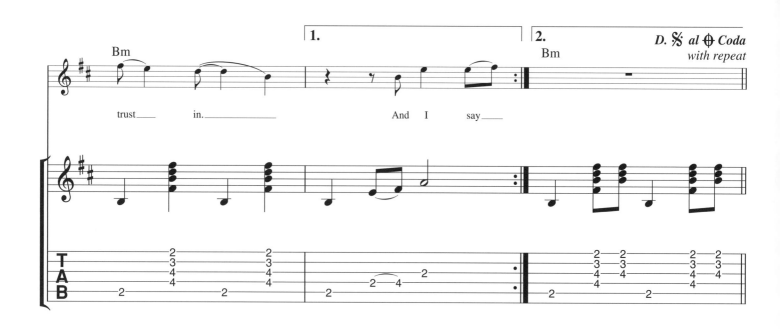

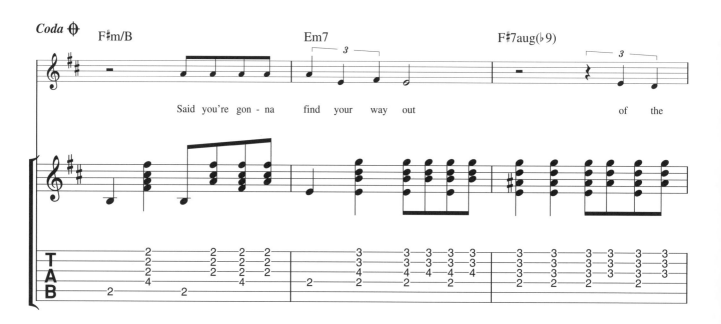

Of the

Verse 2:
Don't let them get you down
Making you feel guilty about
Golden rain will bring you riches
All the good things you deserve now.

Verse 4:
And I say high tide, mid-afternoon
People fly by in the traffic's boom
Knowing just where you're blowing
Getting to where you should be going.

Verse 5 (%):
Day by day your world fades away
Waiting to feel all the dreams that say
Golden rain will bring you riches
All the good things you deserve now.

Verse 6
And I say climbing, forever trying
You're gonna find your way out of the wild, wild wood.
(*To Coda*)

the changingman

WORDS & MUSIC BY PAUL WELLER & BRENDAN LYNCH

Begin fast fade here

* Stanley Road version continues to end

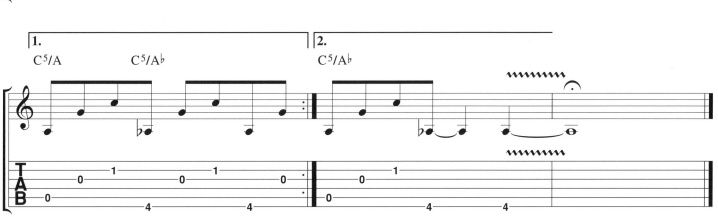

friday street

WORDS & MUSIC BY PAUL WELLER

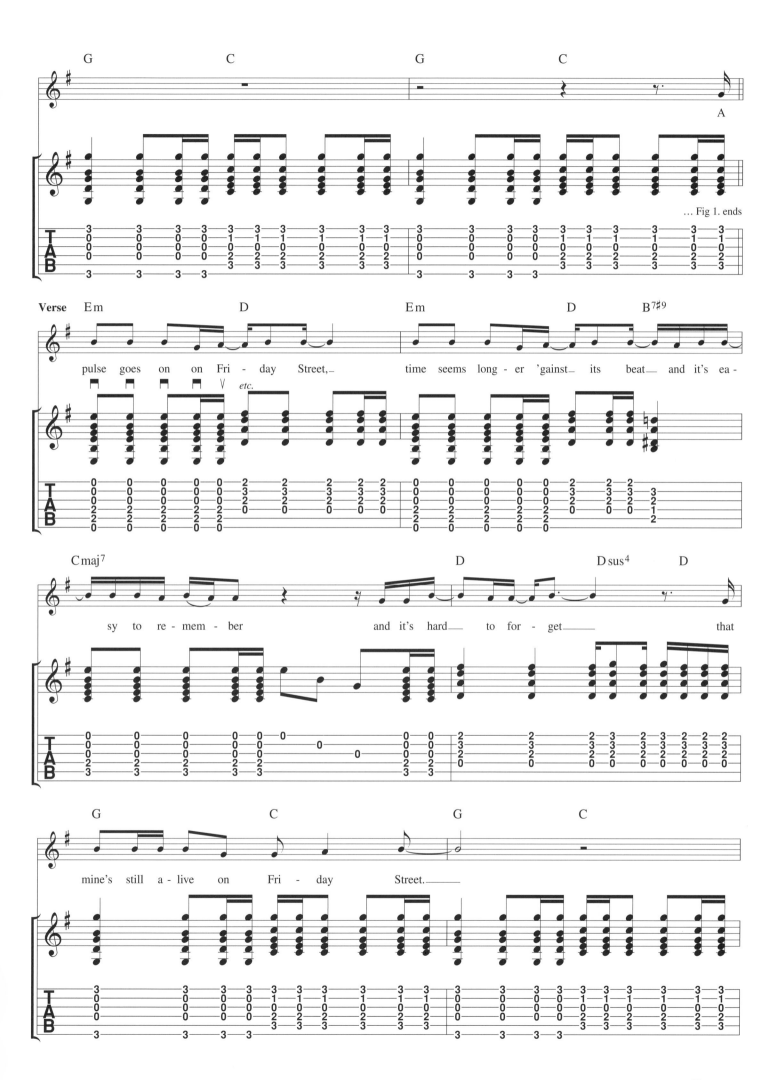

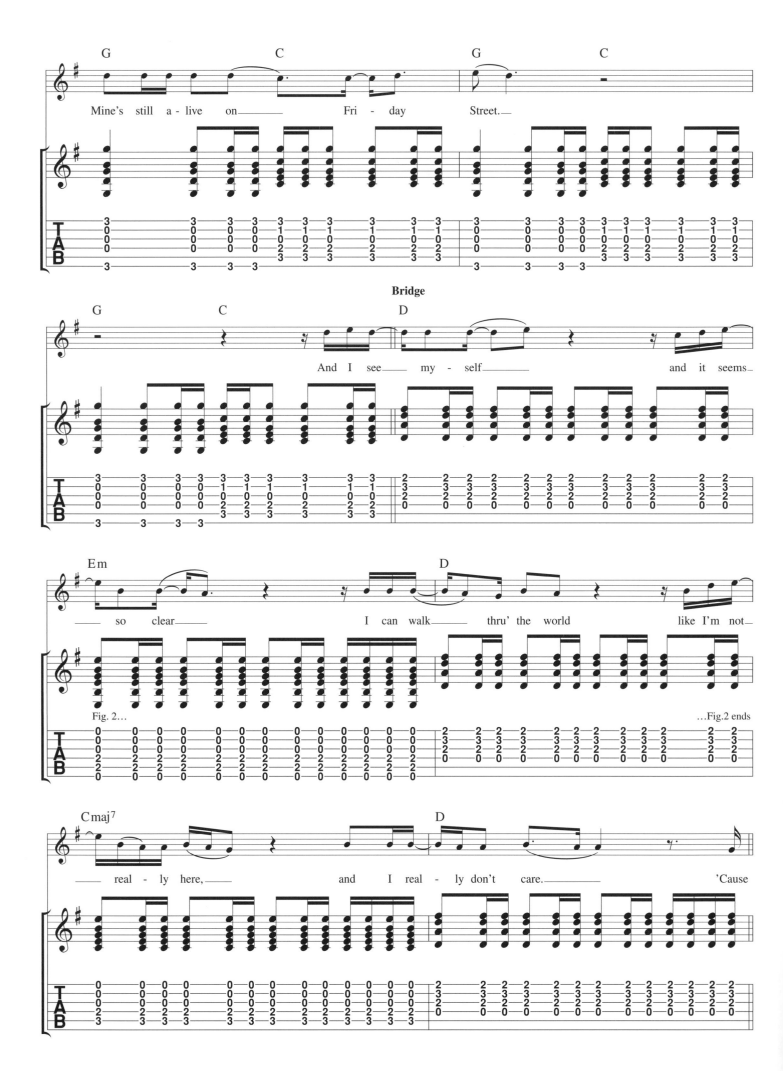

Bridge

Mine's still a-live on Fri-day Street.

And I see my-self and it seems so clear I can walk thru' the world like I'm not real-ly here, and I real-ly don't care. 'Cause

Fig. 2... ...Fig.2 ends

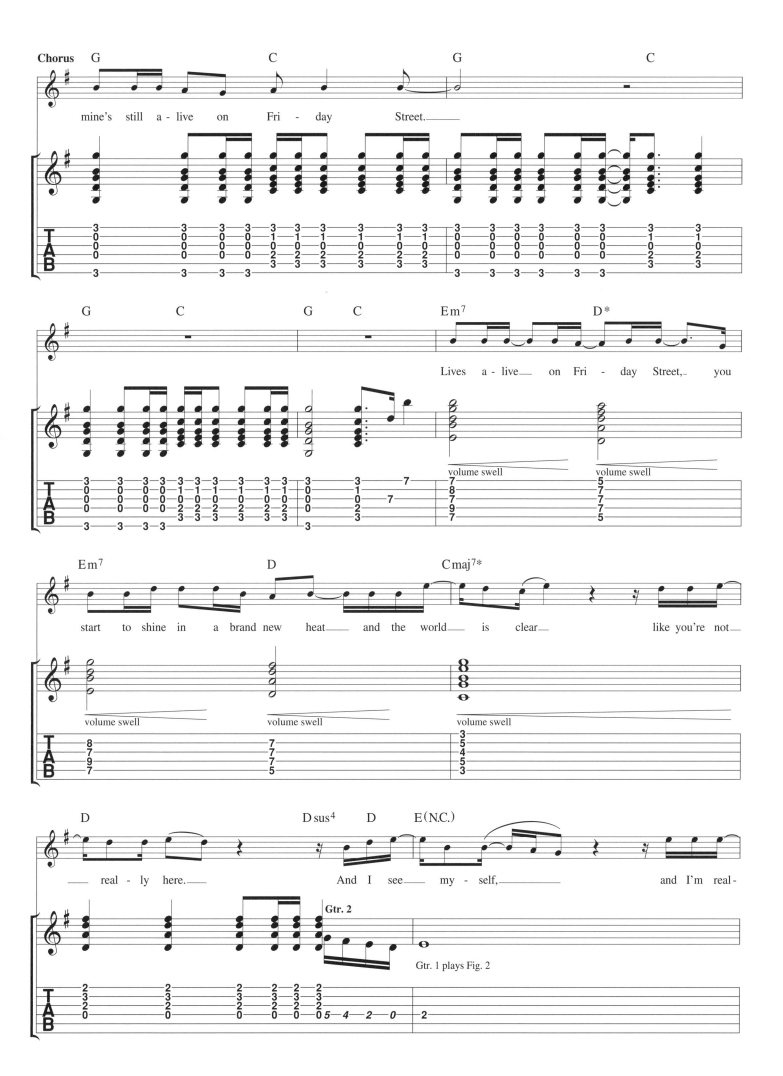

brand new start

WORDS & MUSIC BY PAUL WELLER

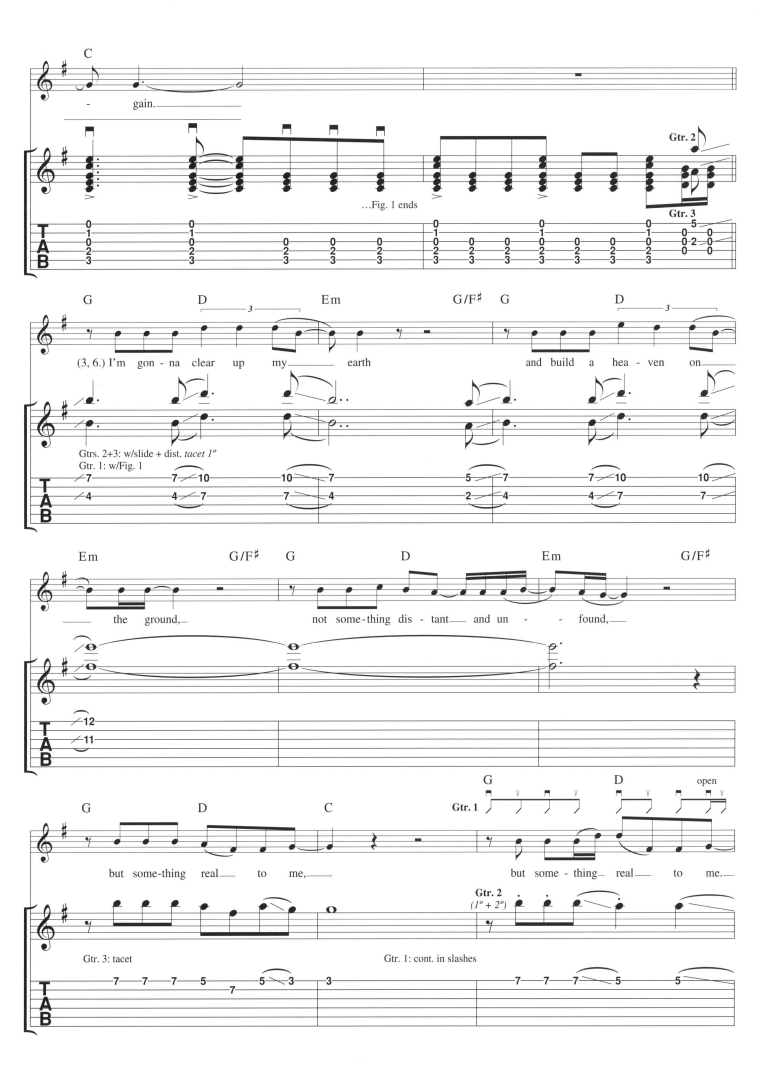

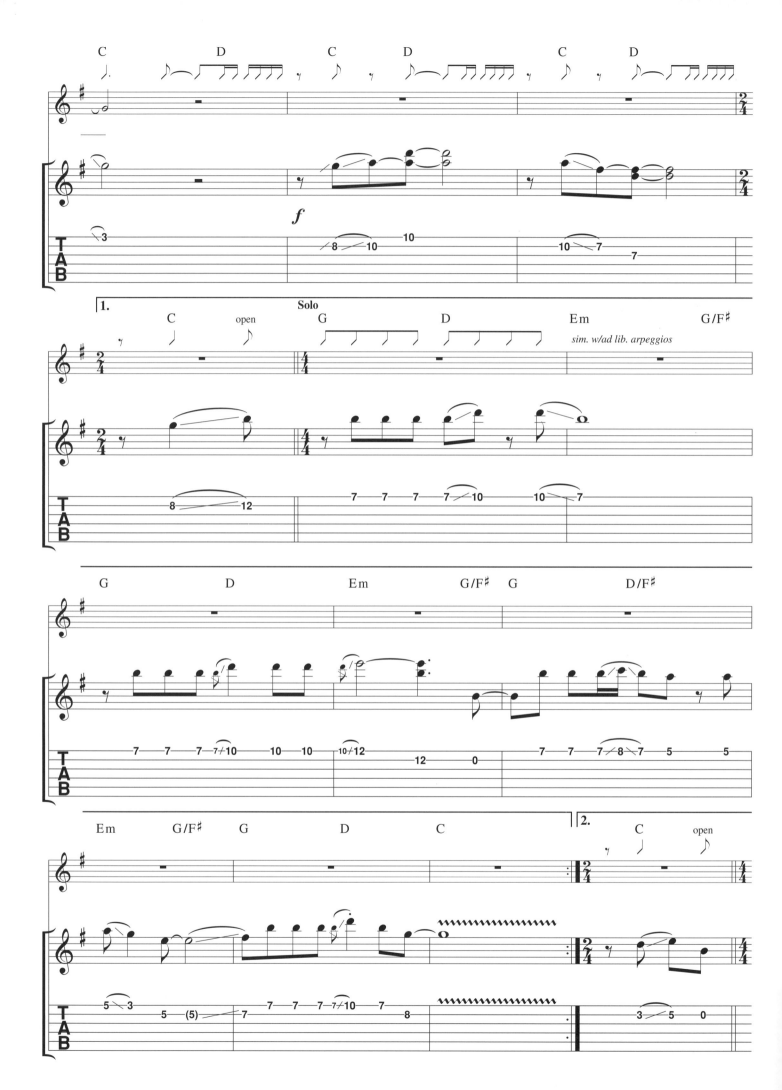

you do something to me

WORDS & MUSIC BY PAUL WELLER

broken stones

WORDS & MUSIC BY PAUL WELLER

Oh— at— such a— cost.—   Like a lo-ser's— reach—

Accordion solo
Bass arr. for Gtr.

And an-oth-er bit

Chorus

shat-ters   oh an-oth-er lit-tle bit get— lost,—   tell me what else real-ly

Keyboards arr. for Gtr.

mermaids

WORDS & MUSIC BY PAUL WELLER

1. She's in my head,
(Verse 3 see block lyric)
she's in my mind,
I of-ten hide

and I'm all she says,
in her ma-gic hair,
yes she knows me well,
and there I learn a-gain

To Coda ⊕

as well as you can.
the joy of life.

1.
2. She's on my side,

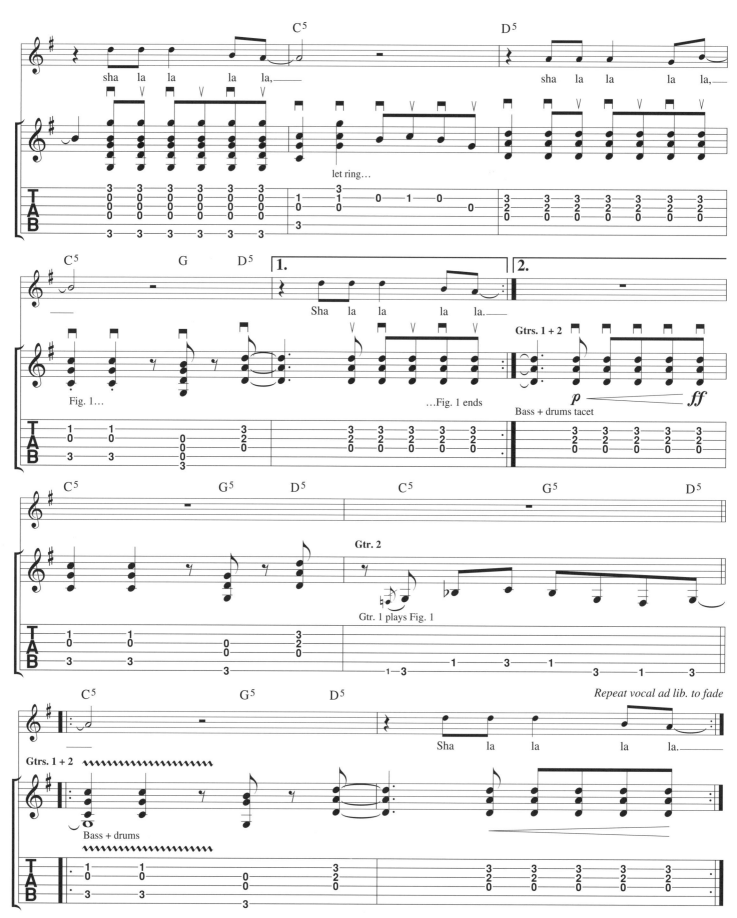

Verse 3:
Come in my head
Come in my mind
You can only love
When you open up to be yourself.

into tomorrow

WORDS & MUSIC BY PAUL WELLER

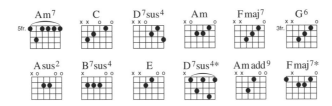

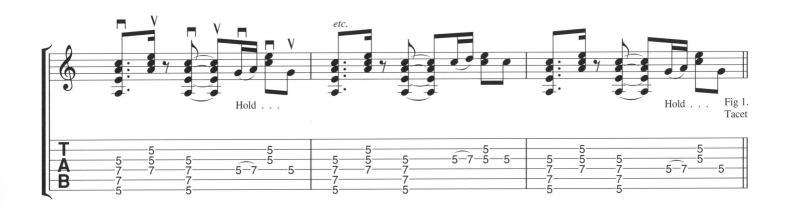

Verse:

1. In-to the mists of time and space where we have no say o-ver date and place oh, yeah.

Fig 2. Hold . . . Hold . . . end Fig 2.

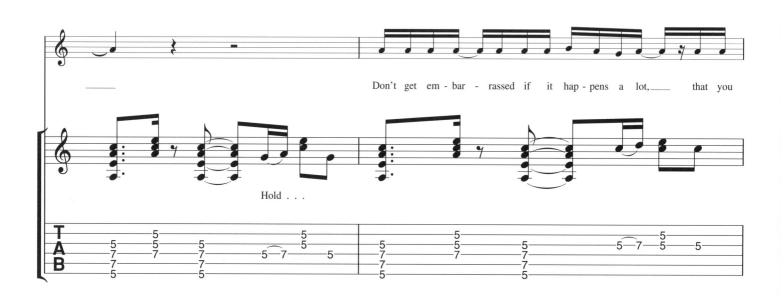

Don't get em-bar-rassed if it hap-pens a lot, that you

Hold . . .

don't know how you start-ed or where you're gon-a stop, oh, yeah. And

Hold . . . Hold . . .

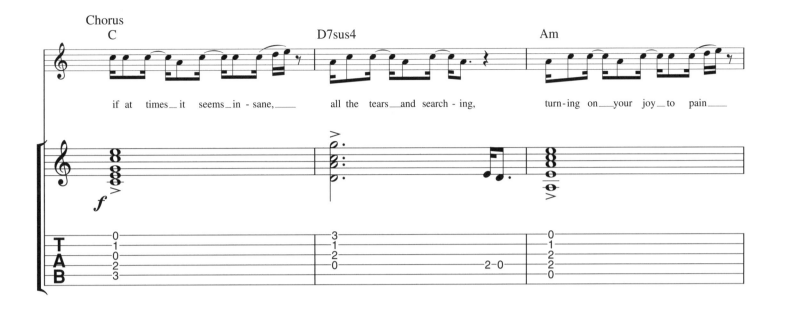

as we head___ in - to to - mor - row.___

Verse:

2. Round and round_like a twist - ed wheel,___ spin-ning at__at - tempt___ to find_____ the feel,___ the_

___ feel,_____ find the path_that will help__ us find a feel - ing of__con - trol__ o - ver lives

Chorus
C

(Final chorus see block lyric)

and minds___ ah, yeah,___ yeah,_yeah, yeah._ And if at times_ it seems_in - sane,

Hold . . .

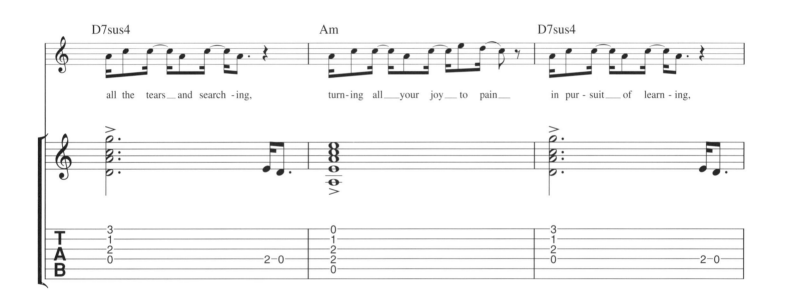

D7sus4   Am   D7sus4

all the tears_and search -ing,   turn-ing all_your joy_ to pain___   in pur - suit_ of learn - ing,

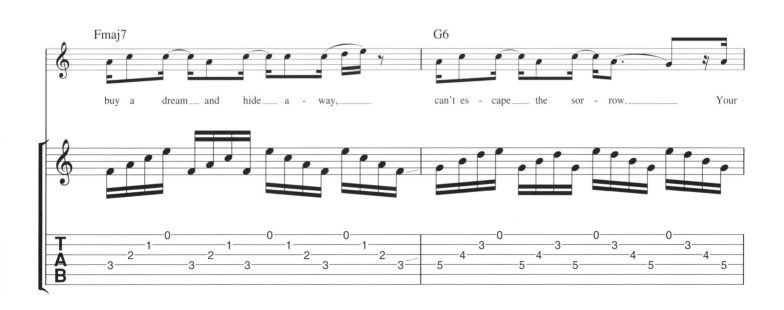

Fmaj7   G6

buy a dream_ and hide_ a - way,_____   can't es - cape_ the sor - row._____ Your

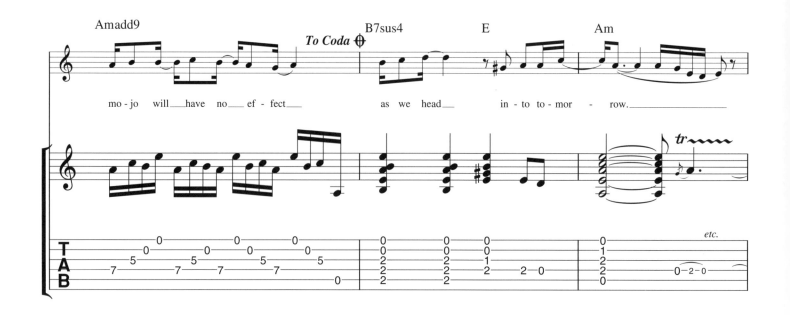

mo - jo   will___ have   no___ ef - fect___   as   we   head___   in - to to - mor - row.___

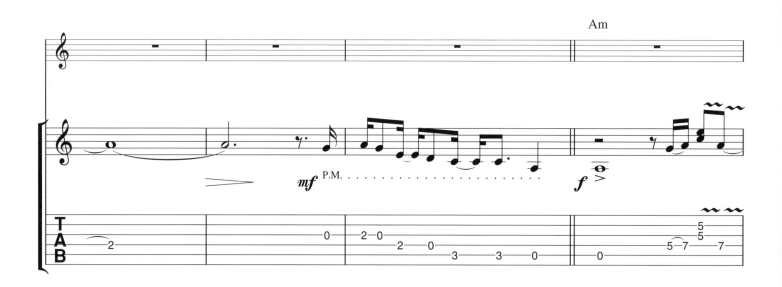

Yeah,___ yeah,   yeah,___   and

Coda ⊕

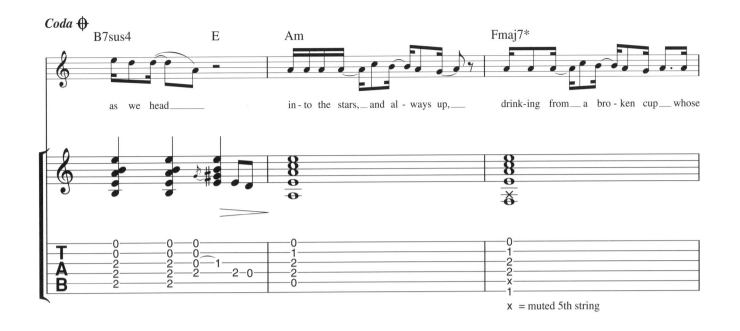

B7sus4   E   Am   Fmaj7*

as we head_____ in - to the stars,__ and al - ways up,__ drink-ing from__ a bro - ken cup__ whose

x = muted 5th string

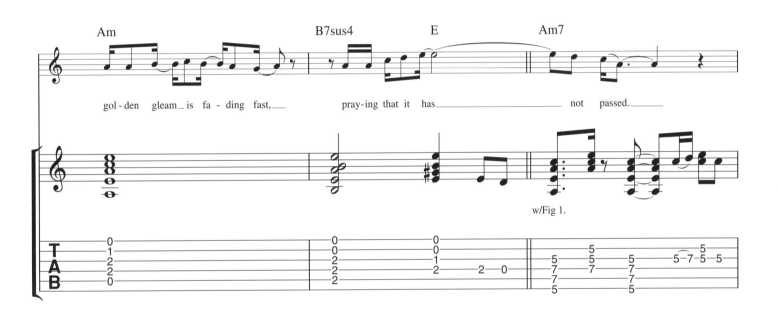

Am   B7sus4   E   Am7

gol - den gleam_ is fa - ding fast,__ pray-ing that it has_____ not passed._____

w/Fig 1.

Oh,____ in - to to - mor-

Hold . . .

Final chorus:

And if at times it seems insane
All the tears and searching
Turning all your joy to pain
In pursuit of learning
Praying that it will connect
Can't escape the sorrow
Your mojo will have no effect
As we head ...

présentation de la tablature de guitare

Il existe trois façons différentes de noter la musique pour guitare : à l'aide d'une portée musicale, de tablatures ou de barres rythmiques.

Les BARRES RYTHMIQUES sont indiquées au-dessus de la portée. Jouez les accords dans le rythme indiqué. Les notes rondes indiquent des notes réciles.

La PORTÉE MUSICALE indique les notes et rythmes et est divisée en mesures. Cette division est représentée par des lignes. Les notes sont : do, ré, mi, fa, sol, la, si.

La PORTÉE EN TABLATURE est une représentation graphique des touches de guitare. Chaque ligne horizontale correspond à une corde et chaque chiffre correspond à une case.

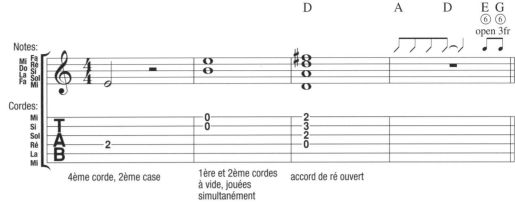

4ème corde, 2ème case

1ère et 2ème cordes à vide, jouées simultanément

accord de ré ouvert

notation spéciale de guitare : définitions

TIRÉ DEMI-TON : Jouez la note et tirez la corde afin d'élever la note d'un demi-ton (étape à moitié).

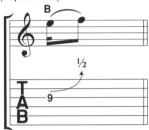

TIRÉ PLEIN : Jouez la note et tirez la corde afin d'élever la note d'un ton entier (étape entière).

TIRÉ D'AGRÉMENT : Jouez la note et tirez la corde comme indiqué. Jouez la première note aussi vite que possible.

TIRÉ QUART DE TON : Jouez la note et tirez la corde afin d'élever la note d'un quart de ton.

TIRÉ ET LÂCHÉ : Jouez la note et tirez la corde comme indiqué, puis relâchez, afin d'obtenir de nouveau la note de départ.

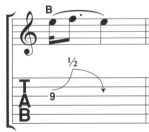

TIRÉ ET REJOUÉ : Jouez la note et tirez la corde comme indiqué puis rejouez la corde où le symbole apparaît.

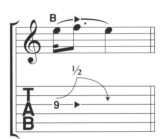

PRÉ-TIRÉ : Tirez la corde comme indiqué puis jouez cette note.

PRÉ-TIRÉ ET LÂCHÉ : Tirez la corde comme indiqué. Jouez la note puis relâchez la corde afin d'obtenir le ton de départ.

HAMMER-ON: Jouez la première note (plus basse) avec un doigt puis jouez la note plus haute sur la même corde avec un autre doigt, sur le manche mais sans vous servir du médiator.

PULL-OFF: Positionnez deux doigts sur les notes à jouer. Jouez la première note et sans vous servir du médiator, dégagez un doigt pour obtenir la deuxième note, plus basse.

GLISSANDO : Jouez la première note puis faites glisser le doigt le long du manche pour obtenir la seconde note qui, elle, n'est pas jouée.

GLISSANDO ET REJOUÉ : Identique au glissando à ceci près que la seconde note est jouée.

HARMONIQUES NATURELLES : Jouez la note tandis qu'un doigt effleure la corde sur le manche correspondant à la case indiquée.

PICK SCRAPE (SCRATCH) : On fait glisser le médiator le long de la corde, ce qui produit un son éraillé.

ÉTOUFFÉ DE LA PAUME : La note est partiellement étouffée par la main (celle qui se sert du médiator). Elle effleure la (les) corde(s) juste au-dessus du chevalet.

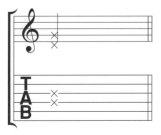

CORDES ÉTOUFFÉES : Un effet de percussion produit en posant à plat la main sur le manche sans relâcher, puis en jouant les cordes avec le médiator.

NOTE: La vitesse des tirés est indiquée par la notation musicale et le tempo.

erläuterung zur tabulaturschreibweise

Es gibt drei Möglichkeiten, Gitarrenmusik zu notieren: im klassichen Notensystem, in Tabulaturform oder als rhythmische Akzente.

RHYTHMISCHE AKZENTE werden über dem Notensystem notiert. Geschlagene Akkorde werden rhythmisch dargestellt. Ausgeschriebene Noten stellen Einzeltöne dar.

Im **NOTENSYSTEM** werden Tonhöhe und rhythmischer Verlauf festgelegt; es ist durch Taktstriche in Takte unterteilt. Die Töne werden nach den ersten acht Buchstaben des Alphabets benannt.
Beachte: "B" in der anglo-amerkanischen Schreibweise entspricht dem deutschen "H"!

DIE TABULATUR ist die optische Darstellung des Gitarrengriffbrettes. Jeder horizontalen Linie ist eine bestimmte Saite zugeordnet, jede Zahl bezeichnet einen Bund.

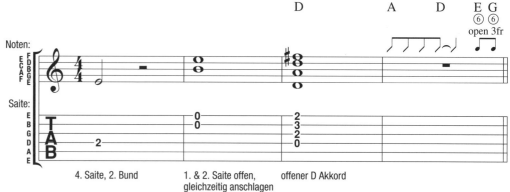

4. Saite, 2. Bund   1. & 2. Saite offen, gleichzeitig anschlagen   offener D Akkord

erklärungen zur speziellen gitarennotation

HALBTON-ZIEHER: Spiele die Note und ziehe dann um einen Halbton höher (Halbtonschritt).

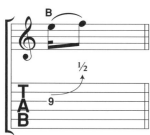

GANZTON-ZIEHER: Spiele die Note und ziehe dann einen Ganzton höher (Ganztonschritt).

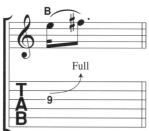

ZIEHER MIT VORSCHLAG: Spiele die Note und ziehe wie notiert. Spiele die erste Note so schnell wie möglich.

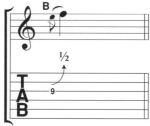

VIERTELTON-ZIEHER: Spiele die Note und ziehe dann einen Viertelton höher (Vierteltonschritt).

ZIEHEN UND ZURÜCKGLEITEN: Spiele die Note und ziehe wie notiert; lasse den Finger dann in die Ausgangsposition zurückgleiten. Dabei wird nur die erste Note angeschlagen.

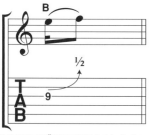

ZIEHEN UND NOCHMALIGES ANSCHLAGEN: Spiele die Note und ziehe wie notiert, schlage die Saite neu an, wenn das Symbol "▶" erscheint und lasse den Finger dann zurückgleiten.

ZIEHER VOR DEM ANSCHLAGEN: Ziehe zuerst die Note wie notiert; schlage die Note dann an.

ZIEHER VOR DEM ANSCHLAGEN MIT ZURÜCKGLEITEN: Ziehe die Note wie notiert; schlage die Note dann an und lasse den Finger auf die Ausgangslage zurückgleiten.

AUFSCHLAGTECHNIK: Schlage die erste (tiefere) Note an; die höhere Note (auf der selben Saite) erklingt durch kräftiges Aufschlagen mit einem anderen Finger der Griffhand.

ABZIEHTECHNIK: Setze beide Finger auf die zu spielenden Noten und schlage die erste Note an. Ziehe dann (ohne nochmals anzuschlagen) den oberen Finger der Griffhand seitlich - abwärts ab, um die zweite (tiefere) Note zum klingen zu bringen.

GLISSANDOTECHNIK: Schlage die erste Note an und rutsche dann mit dem selben Finger der Griffhand aufwärts oder abwärts zur zweiten Note. Die zweite Note wird nicht angeschlagen.

GLISSANDOTECHNIK MIT NACHFOLGENDEM ANSCHLAG: Gleiche Technik wie das gebundene Glissando, jedoch wird die zweite Note angeschlagen.

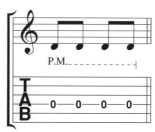

NATÜRLICHES FLAGEOLETT: Berühre die Saite über dem angegebenen Bund leicht mit einem Finger der Griffhand. Schlage die Saite an und lasse sie frei schwingen.

PICK SCRAPE: Fahre mit dem Plektrum nach unten über die Saiten - klappt am besten bei umsponnenen Saiten.

DÄMPFEN MIT DER SCHLAGHAND: Lege die Schlaghand oberhalb der Brücke leicht auf die Saite(n).

DÄMPFEN MIT DER GRIFFHAND: Du erreichst einen percussiven Sound, indem du die Griffhand leicht über die Saiten legst (ohne diese herunterzudrücken) und dann mit der Schlaghand anschlägst.

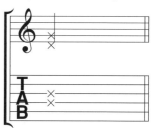

AMMERKUNG: Das Tempo der Zieher und Glissandos ist abhängig von der rhythmischen Notation und dem Grundtempo.

spiegazioni di tablatura per chitarra

La musica per chitarra può essere annotata in tre diversi modi: sul pentagramma, in tablatura e in taglio ritmico

IL TAGLIO RITMICO è scritto sopra il pentagramma. Percuotere le corde al ritmo indicato Le teste arrotondate delle note indicano note singole.

IL PENTAGRAMMA MUSICALE mostra toni e ritmo ed è divisa da linee in settori. I toni sono indicati con le prime sette lettere dell'alfabeto.

LA TABLATURA rappresenta graficamente la tastiera della chitarra. Ogni linea orizzontale rappresenta una corda, ed ogni corda rappresenta un tasto.

4° corda, 2° tasto   1° e 2° corda aperte,   accordo D aperto
suonate insieme

definizioni per annotazioni speciali per chitarra

SEMI-TONO CURVATO: percuotere la nota e curvare di un semitono (1/2 passo).

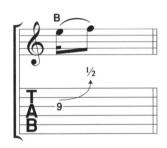

TONO CURVATO: Percuotere la nota e curvare di un tono (passo intero).

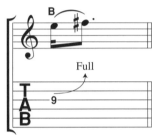

NOTA BREVE, CURVATA: percuotere la nota e curvare come indicato. Suonare la prima nota il più velocemente possibile.

QUARTO DI TONO, CURVATO: Percuotere la nota e curvare di un quarto di passo.

CURVA E LASCIA: Percuotere la nota e curvare come indicato, quindi rilasciare indietro alla nota originale.

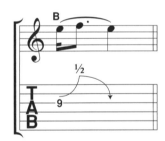

CURVA E RIPERCUOTI: Percuotere la nota e curvare come indicato poi ripercuotere la corda nel punto del simbolo.

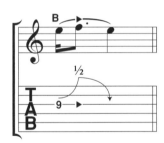

PRE-CURVA: Curvare la nota come indicato e quindi percuoterla.

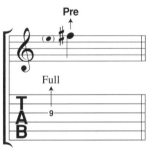

PRE-CURVA E RILASCIO: Curvare la nota come indicato. Colpire e rilasciare la nota indietro alla tonalità indicata.

MARTELLO-COLPISCI: Colpire la prima nota (in basso) con un dito; quindi suona la nota più alta (sulla stessa corda) con un altro dito, toccandola senza pizzicare.

TOGLIERE: Posizionare entrambe le dita sulla nota da suonare. Colpire la prima nota e, senza pizzicare, togliere le dita per suonare la seconda nota (più in basso).

LEGATO SCIVOLATO (GLISSATO): Colpire la prima nota e quindi far scivolare lo stesso dito della mano della tastiera su o giù alla seconda nota. La seconda nota non viene colpita.

CAMBIO SCIVOLATO (GLISSARE E RICOLPIRE): Uguale al legato - scivolato eccetto che viene colpita la seconda nota.

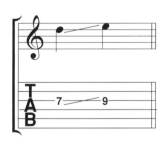

ARMONICA NATURALE: Colpire la nota mentre la mano della tastiera tocca leggermente la corda direttamente sopra il tasto indicato.

PIZZICA E GRAFFIA: Il limite del pizzicato è tirato su (o giù) lungo la corda, producendo un suono graffiante.

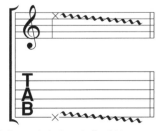

SORDINA CON IL PALMO: La nota è parzialmente attenuata dalla mano del pizzicato toccando la corda (le corde) appena prima del ponte.

CORDE SMORZATE: Un suono di percussione viene prodotto appoggiando la mano della tastiera attraverso la corda (le corde) senza premere, e colpendole con la mano del pizzicato.

NOTA: La velocità di ogni curvatura è indicata dalle annotazioni musicali e dal tempo.

EXCLUSIVE DISTRIBUTORS:
MUSIC SALES LIMITED
8/9 FRITH STREET, LONDON W1V 5TZ, ENGLAND.
MUSIC SALES PTY LIMITED
120 ROTHSCHILD AVENUE, ROSEBERY, NSW 2018,
AUSTRALIA.

ORDER NO.AM957110
ISBN 0-7119-7322-9
THIS BOOK © COPYRIGHT 1998
BY WISE PUBLICATIONS.
VISIT THE INTERNET MUSIC SHOP AT
http://www.musicsales.co.uk

NEW ARRANGEMENTS BY ARTHUR DICK.
NEW MUSIC PROCESSED BY PAUL EWERS
MUSIC DESIGN.

PRINTED IN THE UNITED KINGDOM BY
CALIGRAVING LIMITED, THETFORD, NORFOLK.

YOUR GUARANTEE OF QUALITY:
AS PUBLISHERS, WE STRIVE TO PRODUCE EVERY
BOOK TO THE HIGHEST COMMERCIAL STANDARDS.
THE MUSIC HAS BEEN FRESHLY ENGRAVED AND,
WHILST ENDEAVOURING TO RETAIN THE ORIGINAL
RUNNING ORDER OF THE RECORDED ALBUM,
THE BOOK HAS BEEN CAREFULLY DESIGNED TO
MINIMISE AWKWARD PAGE TURNS AND TO
MAKE PLAYING FROM IT A REAL PLEASURE.
PARTICULAR CARE HAS BEEN GIVEN TO
SPECIFYING ACID-FREE, NEUTRAL-SIZED PAPER
MADE FROM PULPS WHICH HAVE NOT BEEN
ELEMENTAL CHLORINE BLEACHED.
THIS PULP IS FROM FARMED SUSTAINABLE
FORESTS AND WAS PRODUCED WITH SPECIAL
REGARD FOR THE ENVIRONMENT.
THROUGHOUT, THE PRINTING AND BINDING
HAVE BEEN PLANNED TO ENSURE A STURDY,
ATTRACTIVE PUBLICATION WHICH SHOULD GIVE
YEARS OF ENJOYMENT.
IF YOUR COPY FAILS TO MEET OUR HIGH
STANDARDS, PLEASE INFORM US AND WE WILL
GLADLY REPLACE IT.

MUSIC SALES' COMPLETE CATALOGUE
DESCRIBES THOUSANDS OF TITLES AND IS
AVAILABLE IN FULL COLOUR SECTIONS BY
SUBJECT, DIRECT FROM MUSIC SALES LIMITED.
PLEASE STATE YOUR AREAS OF INTEREST AND
SEND A CHEQUE/POSTAL ORDER FOR £1.50 FOR
POSTAGE TO: MUSIC SALES LIMITED,
NEWMARKET ROAD, BURY ST. EDMUNDS,
SUFFOLK IP33 3YB.